Toothless Dragon

The Laidlaw Reading Program LEVEL 6

William Eller

Kathleen B. Hester

S. Elizabeth Davis

Thomas J. Edwards

Roger Farr

Jack W. Humphrey

DayAnn McClenathan

Nancy Lee Roser

Elizabeth M. Ryan

Ann Myra Seaver

Marian Alice Simmons

Margaret Wittrig

Patricia J. Cianciolo, *Children's literature*

David W. Reed, *Linguistics*

LAIDLAW BROTHERS • PUBLISHERS

A Division of Doubleday & Company, Inc.

RIVER FOREST, ILLINOIS

Palo Alto, California   Atlanta, Georgia   Dallas, Texas

New York, New York   Toronto, Canada

Acknowledgments

Atheneum Publishers, Inc., for the poem "Ants Live Here" by Lilian Moore. Text copyright ©
1967 by Lilian Moore. From I FEEL THE SAME WAY. Used by permission of Atheneum
Publishers.

Doubleday & Company, Inc., for an adaptation of "Georgie." From GEORGIE by Robert Bright.
Copyright 1944 by Doubleday & Company, Inc. Reprinted by permission of the publisher.

E. P. Dutton & Co., Inc., for the poem "Dogs" by Marchette Chute. Copyright, 1946, by
Marchette Chute. From the book AROUND AND ABOUT by Marchette Chute. Copyright, ©
1957 by E. P. Dutton & Co., Inc., publishers, and used with their permission.

Rae R. Fairbrother for "Kim and Gus," adapted from "Gerry and Gus." Published originally in
WEE WISDOM magazine. Adapted by permission of Rae R. Fairbrother.

(Acknowledgments continue on page 224.)

Project Director: Ralph J. Cooke
Senior Editor: Helen W. Crane
Editor: Barbara Ryan
Production Director: LaVergne Niequist
Senior Production Editor: Sonja Sola
Production Editor: Angela Zabransky
Art Director: Gloria Muczynski
Art Consultants: Donald Meighan, Don Walkoe
Cover Art: Donald Charles
Illustrators: Angela Adams, Louis Aronson, Marc Belenchia, Bob Binks, Ted Carr, Ralph
          Creasman, Deso Csanady, Pat Doyle, Jack Haesly, Hilary Hayton, Tim and Greg
          Hildebrandt, Edward Huff, Janet LaSalle, Erica Merkling, Joe Rogers, Hans Zander
Photographers: Robert Buchbinder (pp. 27, 157); Grant Heilman (pp. 150, 152 *top*); Mervin
          Larson, Director, Arizona-Sonora Desert Museum (p. 44); Hugh Spencer
          (p. 152 *bottom*); Eileen Tanson (p. 149)

ISBN 0-8445-3418-8
Copyright © 1976 by
Laidlaw Brothers, Publishers
A Division of Doubleday & Company, Inc.

PRINTED IN THE UNITED STATES OF AMERICA

123456789 10 11 12 13 14 15   4321098765

Contents

Hide and Seek

Special Surprise

Most Any Day

Long Ago and Far Away

Georgie

Somewhere in a little town,
there was a little house.
    Way up in this little house,
there was a little room.
    This little room was just right
for Georgie.

    Georgie was a little ghost.
    And like every other ghost,
Georgie liked to play at night.

Every night, about the same time,
Georgie came down the steps.

One

by

one

by

one.

SQUEAK

Georgie was very quiet.

Then one of the steps would squeak.

It was just a little squeak.

Georgie would come to a door.

The door would squeak.

This was a big squeak.

11

It was the same every night.

All was quiet in the house.

Then a little squeak would come
from the step.

And a big squeak would come
from the door.

Right then Mr. and Mrs. Whittaker
knew it was time for bed.

That was not all.

When Mr. and Mrs. Whittaker got up,
Herman got up, too.

He knew it was time
to go outside.

When Herman went outside,
Oliver knew it was time
to get up.
Then he would say,

Wh000o

And so,
night after night
after night
all was the same.

At last Mr. Whittaker
took it into his head to do something.

"I will fix that step," he said.
"I will fix the door, too.
Then we will not have any more squeaks."

Mr. Whittaker went to work.
The step didn't squeak any more.
The door didn't squeak any more.
All was quiet in the house.
No more squeaks!

Now,

Mr. and Mrs. Whittaker didn't know
when to go to bed.

So they just sat.

Herman didn't know
when he should go outside.

So he just sat.

Oliver didn't know
when he should get up
and say,

"Whoo ᵒ ᵒ ᵒ ᵒ ᵒ o!"

So he just sat.

18

As for Georgie, he sat in his room.

This was a fine how-do-you-do!

Why did Georgie sit in his room?
What do you think Georgie will do next?

Home Again

Before long Georgie went to look
for another house.

A house without a ghost.

He ran from this house to that house.

Every house had a ghost.
All but one.
It was a fine old house.
It was Mr. Groan's house.
And what a house it was!

The big door groaned so.
The steps groaned so.
And Mr. Groan groaned so!

Mr. Groan groaned so much
that Georgie just had to get away.
So he looked for another place
to live.

At last Georgie found a place.

But Moo lived there.

Moo was not much fun.

She didn't even want to play.

Georgie was not happy.

He didn't know what to do.

He didn't know where to go.

Georgie sat around.
He didn't even want
to play at night.

Then one day Oliver came
to see Georgie.

"Come on home to Mr. Whittaker's,"
he called.

"Come and see what I have found.
The step squeaks again.
The door squeaks again.
All the squeaks are back."

Georgie ran right home.

That very night, at the same old time,
Georgie came down the steps.

One

　　by

　　　one

　　　　by

　　　　　one.

He was very quiet.

SQUEAK

Then squeak went the step.

It was just a little squeak.

Squeak went the door.

This was a big squeak.

Once again,

Mr. and Mrs. Whittaker know
when to go to bed.

Herman knows when it is time
to go outside.

As for Oliver, he knows
when it is time to get up and say,

Some One

Some one came knocking
　At my wee, small door;
Some one came knocking,
　I'm sure—sure—sure;
I listened, I opened,
　I looked to left and right,
But nought there was a-stirring
　In the still dark night;
Only the busy beetle
　Tap-tapping in the wall,
Only from the forest
　The screech-owl's call,
Only the cricket whistling
　While the dew drops fall,
So I know not who came knocking,
　At all, at all, at all.

Walter de la Mare

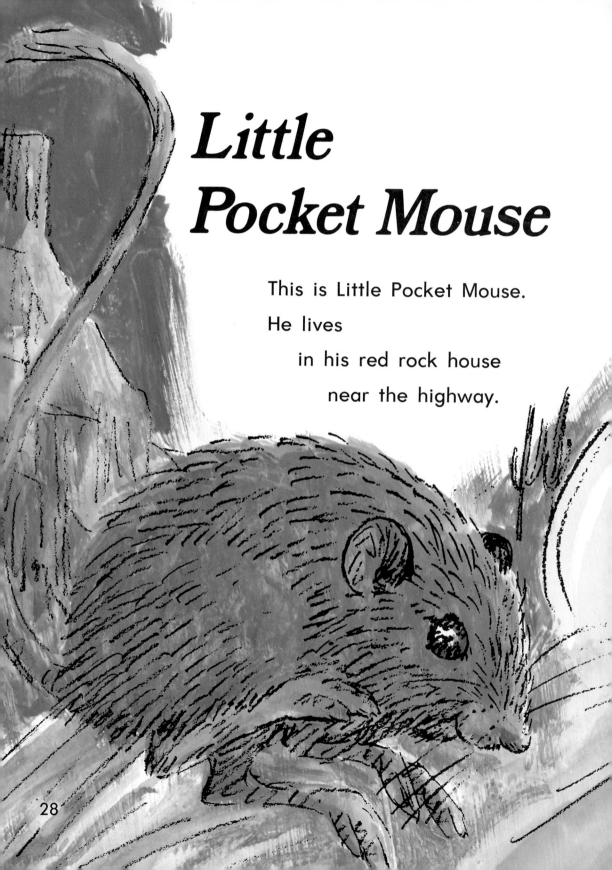

Little Pocket Mouse

This is Little Pocket Mouse.
He lives
in his red rock house
near the highway.

28

One night Little Pocket Mouse
came out of his red rock house.
He ran down to the highway
just as he did every other night.
He wanted to see the cars go by.
He wanted to run in the light
from a car.

All at once a car came to a stop.
A man and a boy got out.

"Oh, no!" said the man
when he looked at the tire.
"Now we will be here for a while."

Little Pocket Mouse was not far
from the light.
But no one could see him.
He just sat.

"This is not a good place to stop,"
said the man.

"But we have to fix that tire."

The boy looked up and down the highway.
"We were here once before," he said.
"This is where we saw a mouse.

Not far from that red rock.

I would like to see another mouse."

"Don't look for it now," said his father.
"Not while I'm fixing this tire.

Come and help me."

The boy put his coat down so he could help.

Little Pocket Mouse was not far away.
"They don't know what I am," he thought.
"I'm not just any old mouse.
I'm a pocket mouse!"

He ran over to the boy's coat.
In he went.
Just to look around.
Little Pocket Mouse was quiet.
No one knew he was there.

After a while the man said,
"The tire is fixed, now.
Get your coat and come on.
We have to get to the airport."

So away they went . . .
the man and the boy in the car
and Little Pocket Mouse
in the coat.

"I'm not just any mouse,"
he thought.
"I'm a pocket mouse.
And I'm going
to the airport!"

33

Before long the man and the boy
were at the airport.
They did not know
about Little Pocket Mouse.
But he was there, too.

High in the Sky

At last they were all in a plane . . .

the man

the boy

and Little Pocket Mouse.

The big plane took off.
Soon it was high in the sky.

Little Pocket Mouse
was in the boy's coat.
No one could see him.
No one knew he was there.

After a little while,
he crawled out.
He looked around
and saw some food.
That was just
what he wanted.
So he jumped.

"E-e-eek!" said a girl.
"A mouse.
Get him off!"

Little Pocket Mouse
jumped again.

He ran in and out
between the feet.

He wanted a place
to hide.

"E-e-eek!" said a woman.
"A mouse.
Catch him!"

Little Pocket Mouse ran fast.
In and out between the feet.
He was looking for a place
to hide.
He was looking for the coat
when the boy saw him.

"Don't step on him,"
said the boy.
"He's a pocket mouse!"

39

Little Pocket Mouse sat up tall.

"Now that boy knows
what I am," he thought.
"I'm not just any old mouse.
I'm a pocket mouse!"

40

The boy put the little mouse
in his coat pocket.

Little Pocket Mouse was happy
to be back in there.

This time he wanted to hide,
not just to look around.

"How did that pocket mouse
get in this plane?" asked the man.

"I think I know," said the boy.
"I know where he lives, too.
Back there where we fixed the tire.
Let's take him there, Dad."

So they did.

Now Little Pocket Mouse is home again.
He lives
    in his red rock house
        near the highway.

How do you think Little Pocket Mouse
got back home?

POCKET MOUSE

Any kind of mouse can get into a pocket.

But there is one kind of mouse that has pockets.

The kind of mouse that has pockets

is called a pocket mouse.

Where are the pockets?

44

The pocket mouse lives in a place
that is dry all the time.
It can't get all the water it wants
because the place is so dry.
It gets water from the food it eats.

The pocket mouse sleeps all day long.
It comes out at night to eat and play.
Sometimes you can see it running
in the light from a car.

45

LITTLE HIPPO

Every morning was the same
for Little Hippo.

All the big hippos would wait
for him to get up.

They wanted to take care of him.

After Little Hippo was up,
he was never by himself.
Someone was always around
to take care of him.

If Little Hippo wanted food,
Big Charles would see that he got it.

"Little Hippo wants some food,"
Big Charles would call.
"Bring it over here."

The big hippos would do just that.
Then they would wait
for Little Hippo to eat.

One morning Little Hippo said to himself,

"I don't want anyone to bring me food.

I don't want anyone to take care of me.

I just want to be by myself.

Even if it is only for a little while.

When no one is looking, I will run away."

Little Hippo waited for a while.

When he thought no one was looking,
he began to walk away.

But Big Charles saw him.

"Little Hippo, come back here," he called.

"When will you learn not to go off
by yourself?"

"Why can't I go off by myself?"
asked Little Hippo.

"Why can't I do something by myself?"

He was not happy.

Little Hippo thought and thought.
"I know what I will do," he said.
"I will see what my friends do
when they want to get away."

It didn't take long for Little Hippo
to learn one thing.
Every one of his friends
had a hiding place.

Little Hippo was the only one
who didn't have his own place.
"Where can I hide?" he asked.

Just then Big Charles called,
"Let's play a game.
All of you go and hide.
I will come and find you."

"Oh, good!" said Little Hippo.
"Now I can find a hiding place
of my very own."

Why did Little Hippo want to go off
by himself?

Little Hippo ran over to the tall trees.
But when he got there,
he found some other hippos.

Little Hippo ran to the pond.

But when he got there, he found some more hippos.

Little Hippo walked away.

"I'm going to find my own hiding place," he said.

"A place where I can be by myself.

A place where no one can find me.

It will be my secret hiding place.

I will be the only hippo who knows about it."

The Secret Hiding Place

Little Hippo walked along
until he came to a rock.

"Maybe I can hide under that,"
he said.

Before long a lion came by.

"Funny Little Hippo," said the lion.

"That's no place to hide.

Come with me.

You can hide in my house."

Little Hippo ran after the lion.
"Will we get to your house soon?" he asked.

"Yes," said the lion.
"Here is my house.
  You can stay in here.
  Go right in and make yourself at home.
  I'm going to find something to eat.
  Don't go away until I get back."

Little Hippo was very quiet
as he sat in the lion's house.
It was like night in there.
Little Hippo was afraid to walk around.
He was sure that someone was
in the house with him.

"I don't like this hiding place,"
he said.
"I don't want to stay in here.
I'm going to get out.
Fast!"

Little Hippo ran out
of the lion's house.

He ran for a long, long time.

He ran in and out between the trees.

He didn't know where he was going.

He wanted Big Charles.

Little Hippo was afraid.

At last Little Hippo stopped.
He sat down all by himself.
He could run no more.

Soon a tiny voice called out,
"What are you doing here,
Little Hippo?"

Little Hippo looked around
and saw one of his friends.
"I'm afraid I'm lost," he said.
"I can't find my way home."

Little Hippo's friend laughed.
"You can't be lost," he said.
"Look down there and tell me
what you see."

Little Hippo looked down.
There were the other hippos
looking for him!
They were looking all around.
But not one of them
was looking up.

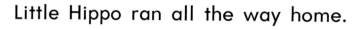

Little Hippo ran all the way home.

He was happy to get back.

He was happy to see Big Charles
and the other hippos.

And they were happy to see him.

"Where were you hiding?"
they asked Little Hippo.
"No one could find you."

Little Hippo just looked
at the big hippos.
He didn't say anything.

"I have a secret hiding place
of my very own," he thought.
"And I'm not going to tell anyone
about it.
It's a place where I can be by myself."

A Ghost Letter

Do you want to learn how to write
a ghost letter?
This is what you will need.

Write your letter this way.
Then let it dry.

Now do you want to learn
how to read your letter?
Put it over a light
and wait for a while.
See what you can find out.

I am
a good ghost.

Special Surprise

Tom's Surprise

Tom was at Grandma's house
and was going to stay for the night.
He liked to be with Grandma and Grandpa.
They were always doing something
to surprise him.
So Tom wanted to surprise them.
But how?

Grandma came into the room.

"Look at this," she said.
"A cookie jar.
Just what we need."

"We have a cookie jar,"
said Grandpa.
"Why do we need another one?"

"We can't put cookies
in that old jar," said Grandma.
"Don't you remember what we did with it?"

"I sure do," laughed Grandpa.

Tom could remember when the old jar
had held cookies.

"I still wish there were cookies
in it," he said to himself.

Before Tom went to bed,
he looked in the paper.

"Now I know how I can surprise
Grandma and Grandpa!" he said.
"They need a cookie jar.
I know where to buy one for them."

Tom went to sleep still thinking
about the old jar that had held
all kinds of cookies.

The next day Grandma took Tom home.

"I can't stay very long," she said.
"I want to make some cookies for Grandpa."

As soon as Grandma had gone,
Tom ran to find his mother.

"Hey, Mom," he called.
"I want to buy something
to surprise Grandma and Grandpa.
They need a cookie jar.
Grandma said so.
She saw one in the paper.
Can I buy it for her?
I have my own money."

Tom's mother smiled at him.

"I don't see why not," she said.
"That would make Grandma and Grandpa
very happy."

"Can we go to the store now?" asked Tom.
"We should get there right away, Mom.
Before all the cookie jars are gone."

"I guess so," said his mother.
"Get your money, Tom.
If we hurry, the cookie jar
may still be there."

Tom and his mother walked to the store.
They went up the elevator to the place
where the cookie jars should be.

"You can buy the cookie jar
by yourself," said Tom's mother.
"After you pay for it, come back here.
Wait for me by the elevator.
I want to buy some other things.
I will not be gone long.
So just wait."

Tom smiled and said,
"OK, Mom."

BIG
SALE
TODAY

Grandma's Surprise

Tom walked over to the cookie jars.
He saw many things that he wanted,
but he didn't stop to look at them.
He was in a hurry.

A lady came up to him
and asked, "May I help you?"

"I want a cookie jar," said Tom.
"It's for my grandma and grandpa.
I want the one with the big smile.
I can pay for it myself.
Here's my money."

The lady smiled at Tom
as she took his money.
Then she put the cookie jar
into a big bag.

"Here's your cookie jar," she said.
"And here's the money you get back."

"Good!" said Tom. "I have money left.
There's enough left over
to buy something for myself."

Tom went back to the elevator,
but his mother wasn't there.

"I will look around until she comes,"
he said.

He saw many things . . .
    games,
       and cars,
          and planes.
Even bikes!

Tom looked at his money.
There wasn't enough money left
to pay for any of the things
he saw!

73

Tom's mother was waiting
by the elevator.

"Didn't you find
the cookie jar?" she asked.

"I sure did," said Tom.
"The same one that was
in the paper.
It's a happy cookie jar, Mom.
Because it has a smile.
Grandma and Grandpa
will like it."

"Where is it?"
asked his mother.
"What did you do
with the bag?"

Tom looked down
and all around.

"Oh, no!" he cried.
"The lady gave it to me.
I know she did.
Mom, I just have to find it!"

"Where did you go
after you got the cookie jar?"
she asked.

"I walked around
and looked at the bikes
and other things," said Tom.
"The cookie jar
was in a paper bag.
But I don't remember
where I put it.
What will I do?"

Tom's mother said, "Let's go back
to the places where you were looking."

So they walked back . . .
    to the bikes,
      and the planes,
        and the cars,
          and the games.
The paper bag wasn't any place!

"What will we do?" cried Tom.

Just then he saw the lady
who had helped him.

"Didn't you forget this?" she asked.

Tom smiled at the lady and said,
"I guess I did. Thank you very much."

He took the paper bag and said,
"Let's go right home, Mom.
Before I forget again."

That night Tom went over
to his grandma's house.

When Grandma came to the door
he cried, "Surprise! Surprise!"

Tom gave the bag to Grandma
and said, "Open it up, Grandma.
Open it now."

Grandma laughed when she looked
in the bag.

"What a good surprise!" she said.
"How did you know that I wanted
a cookie jar?"

Then she smiled and said,
"Thank you, Tom. Come on in.
I have a surprise for you, too."

What do you think Grandma's surprise was?

Robber in the Woods

There was a big old house
near the woods.
For a long time no one lived in it.

Then one day a family came
to live in the house—
Mr. and Mrs. Newman,
their boy, Jim,
and their girl, Betsy.

The Newman family liked the house
near the woods.
They liked to live in the country.

"My, it's quiet out here!" said Mrs. Newman.

"It's so quiet it's spooky!" said Jim.

One night the Newman family
was looking at TV.

"What's that?" asked Betsy.

"What's what?" asked Jim.

"That noise," said Betsy.
"I hear something funny."

"It's only the TV," said Jim.

82

"No," said Betsy. "I hear a noise outside.
It's spooky out here in the country."

"Listen!" said Jim. "I hear a noise, too."

"I don't hear anything," said Mr. Newman.

"I don't hear anything," said Mrs. Newman.
"And it's time both of you were in bed."

Jim and Betsy went to bed.
But soon Jim came running out
of his room.

"Listen!" he cried.
"What's that?"

"What's what?" asked Betsy.

"That noise outside!" said Jim.

"I hear it, too," said Betsy.

"I thought I told both of you
to go to sleep," called Mrs. Newman.

84

Just then there was another noise.

Bang! Bang! Bang!

It came from the back of the house.

Mr. Newman put the lights on.
Everyone ran outside
to see what had made the noise.

No one was there.

"I told you it was spooky out here
in the country," said Jim.

Then Mrs. Newman saw the trash can.
It was on its side.
Trash was all over the yard.

"Who did that?" she cried.

"Maybe it was a ghost!" said Jim.

"I'm scared!" said Betsy.

"Don't be scared," said Mr. Newman.
"I think the wind did this."

The next night the Newman family
was looking at TV again.

All at once Jim said,
"What's that noise?"

"I hear it, too!" said Betsy.
"It's out in the yard.
Near the woods.
And it's not the wind."

"I'm scared," said Jim.

"Me, too," said Betsy.
"I think a robber is out there."

Mr. and Mrs. Newman looked
out the window.

"Oh, no!" cried Mrs. Newman.
"The trash is all over the yard again.
The wind didn't do that."

"A robber did!" said Betsy.
"A robber is trying to get into the house."

"I'm going out to look around,"
said Mr. Newman.

Mr. Newman opened the door
and went outside.
He walked all around the house.

"There's nothing here," he said
to himself.

Then something ran out of the yard
and into the woods.

"Shoo! Shoo!" cried Mr. Newman.

He went back into the house.

"There is something out there," he said.
"But it's nothing to be scared of."

Dinner Time

The very next night
the Newmans were eating dinner.

"There's that spooky noise again,"
said Betsy. "Listen!"

Mr. Newman looked up.
Then he walked to the window.

Soon he began to laugh.

"Come over here, all of you,"
he called. "Here is our robber."

And there it was
right outside
the window!

"Well, Robber," said Jim.
"Are you looking at us?"

90

Who could the robber be?

"That's not a robber," said Betsy.
"That's only a raccoon."

"He looks like a robber," said Jim.
"Let's call him Robber Raccoon."

Mr. Newman opened the door.

"I won't have that robber
around my trash can," he said.

"What are you going to do?"
cried Betsy. "He's just a little raccoon."

"Maybe he was looking for food," said Jim.

Betsy thought for a while.
Then she said, "Let's put some food out
for him every night.
Maybe he won't get into the trash if we do.
Then he can stay around."

Mrs. Newman laughed.

"That might help," she said.
"We will try it for one night."

"All right," said Mr. Newman.
"We might as well give it a try."

So the next night Betsy put out food
for the raccoon.

"Oh, Robber," she said to herself.
"Don't go near the trash can.
If you do, you can't stay."

"Put some food by the window," said Jim.
"He won't be scared to sit there."

Betsy was right about Robber.
The raccoon didn't go near the trash can.
He came to the window and found the food.
Then he sat looking at TV while he ate.

After that, Robber came every night
and ate the food.

And so they all had a TV dinner—
Mr. and Mrs. Newman,
Jim and Betsy Newman,
and Robber Raccoon!

Kim
and
Gus

Kim looked out the window.
There was snow all around,
and it was cold outside.
This was the kind of night
to stay inside.

Kim's mom and dad had gone out
for a while. Grandma was sleeping.
The house was quiet.

All at once Kim heard a noise.

"Woof! Woof!"

At first she thought it was the TV.

Then she heard the noise again.

"Woof! Woof! Woof!"

Kim went to look
out the window.
There in the cold snow sat
a black and white dog.

Kim wanted to bring the dog inside
for a while. It looked so cold.
But she was afraid.
The dog might bring snow into the house.

The dog gave another "woof."

Kim ran to open the door.
The dog just sat and looked at her.

"Oh, come on in, Gus," she said.
"But you must stay on this mat."

Kim had called the dog Gus,
but she didn't know why.

Kim went to find something
for Gus to eat.
Soon she came back with some food.

There was Gus
     on the mat
          where she had left him.

Gus ate all the food.
Then he lay down and looked
at Kim.

Kim didn't know what to do
about Gus. She liked him.
But she knew it wasn't right
to keep him.
So she opened the door
and told him to leave.

"Go home, Gus," she said.
Kim didn't want Gus to go,
but he went anyway.

Just as Kim sat down,
she heard a "woof, woof."
She ran to open the door
and in walked Gus.
He went right over to the mat
and lay down.

"Now, Gus," she said.
"I know I can't keep you.
You must belong to someone.
But who?"

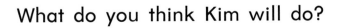

What do you think Kim will do?

Kim didn't want
to make Gus leave again.
So she let him stay inside.

"You can belong to me
for a little while," she said.

Kim went into the next room.
Gus walked in right after her.
And there they were . . .
    fast asleep . . .
        when Mom and Dad came home.

Kim's mom and dad were surprised
to find the dog with her.

"Woof! Woof!" said Gus.
He was not asleep now.

"How did you get in our house?"
cried Kim's mother.

"Who let you in?" asked her dad.

Gus gave another big "woof."
He wasn't going to let them
near Kim. She was his friend.

Kim heard the noise and jumped up.

"Please don't make him go away,"
she cried. "He wants to stay here.
His name is Gus. Oh, please let him stay!"

"You know we can't keep Gus,"
said Kim's mother. "He's not our dog.
But he can stay until morning.
Then we will try to find out
who he belongs to."

Little Surprise

Kim was the first one up
the next morning.
She was very quiet
as she went down the steps.

There was Gus
on the mat
where she had left him.

Gus was not asleep.
He heard Kim
and put his head up.

Kim walked over to Gus.

"Don't you remember me?"
she asked. Then she stopped.

"Oh, no!" she cried.
"Wait until Mom and Dad
see this!"

"Mom! Dad! Grandma!
Come here!" she called.
"Gus isn't a he!
Gus is a she!
And she's got pups!"

Mom and Dad came running
down the steps. Grandma came, too.
They didn't know what Kim was trying
to tell them.
But when they saw Gus, they knew.

"Oh, my!" said Grandma.

"I thought Gus looked big,"
said Kim's mother.

"We can't make her leave now,"
said Kim. "Not with four little pups."

"Someone may be looking
for a lost dog," said Dad.
"We must find out who she belongs to."

"Someone will be surprised
about the pups," said Kim.

Kim didn't say much that morning.
All she could think about was Gus.
She wanted to keep her,
but she knew she couldn't.

Soon Kim heard a man talking on TV.
He said something about a lost dog.
A black and white one.
The dog's name was Henrietta.

Gus was black and white.
Gus was lost, too. Could Gus be Henrietta?

Kim didn't want to call the man.
But she knew she should.
She told him all about Gus.
But she didn't say anything about the pups.

Before long the man came to the house.
Kim wasn't too happy to see him.
But Henrietta was!

The man smiled
when he saw the pups.
Then he smiled at Kim.

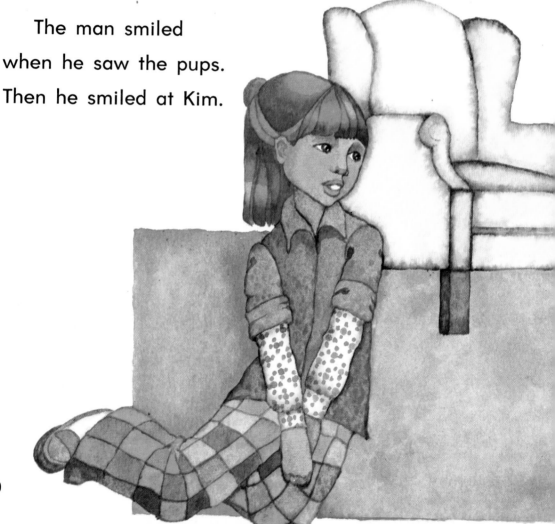

"I would like to do something
to thank you," said the man.
"You took good care of Henrietta.
How would you like one of her pups
when it gets big enough?"

Kim looked at Mom.
Mom looked at Dad.
Dad looked at Mom.
They looked at Kim.

"OK," they said.

Kim saw the very pup she wanted.
It looked just like Henrietta.

"You belong to me," she said.
"I will call you Gus.
But if you have pups,
I will call you Gusetta."

Dogs

The dogs I know
Have many shapes.
For some are big and tall,

And some are long,

And
some
are thin,
And some are fat and small.

And some are little bits of fluff
And have no shape at all.

Marchette Chute

Just for Manuel

Manuel liked school.
At school he had a place of his own
where he could sit and work.
That was his special place.

At school Manuel had a place
to put his coat.
He always put his coat there.
That was Manuel's special place, too.

But at home there was
no special place for Manuel.
His home was in an apartment building.
The building was old.
The apartment was very small.

At home he had to share everything.
He had to share a bed
with his brother Carlos.

His two big brothers had to share
a bed in the same room.

His mother and sister had to share
a bed in another room.
It was a very small room.

One day Manuel said, "Mother,
I need a place at home."

Mother was putting on her coat.
"What place?" she asked.

"A place where I can keep
my things," he said.
"A special place of my very own.
A place I don't have to share.
I need a place just for me."

Manuel's brothers laughed
when they heard him talking.
His sister laughed, too.

"Where will you find
a place?" asked Carlos.
"Will you find a place
under the bed?"

"No," said Manuel.
"There is no room under there
for me."

"You keep looking,"
said his mother.
"You will find a place."

Manuel smiled.
His mother smiled.
Then she went to work.

Manuel's big brothers
went to work, too.
His sister went to the store.
Carlos went out to play.
Now Manuel was all by himself.

Manuel walked around the apartment.
Where could he find a place?
He looked into every room.
Then he saw the table.
Would that make a good place?

He took everything off the table
and put something over it.
Now he had a good place.

Manuel sat under the table.
He liked his special place.
He could play there
and just be by himself.

Before long his sister
came home from the store.
She saw Manuel under the table.

"What are you doing
down there?" she asked.

"Go away," said Manuel. "This is my place."

"This is not your place," said his sister.
"We need the table for dinner."

Manuel went out of the apartment.
He took his things with him
and sat down by Mr. Grubb's door.

He began to play.
He made so much noise
that Mr. Grubb opened his door.

"Go away, Manuel," he said.
"I work at night. I sleep all day.
You make too much noise,
and I can't sleep."

Manuel took all of his things
and went home.

Once again he walked
around the apartment.
He went from room to room.
Then he saw just what he wanted.

"That corner would make
a good place," he said.

Manuel put his things in the corner.
Then he went in and sat down.
The corner was not too big.
It was not too small.
It was just right.

Before long his brothers came home.
"You found a good place," said Carlos.

Soon Mother came.
She saw Manuel in the corner.

"I found a place," he told her.

Mother smiled.
"I knew you would," she said.

And that night he ate his dinner
in the corner.
It was his special place.

125

What Am I?

1. I can eat and drink.
   But I cannot walk.

2. It has four feet on the floor.
   And four feet not on the floor.

3. They can go to the pond.
   But they cannot drink.

4. It never eats.
   It never drinks.
   But it talks and sings.

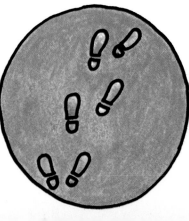

Most Any Day

Lee's Birthday

Lee jumped out of bed.
She knew this would be a good day.
So she was very happy.

Last night she had gone to bed
thinking only good thoughts.
Lee had said to herself over and over,
"Tomorrow is my special day.
Tomorrow is my birthday."

And now tomorrow was today!

Lee opened her closet door.
"Let me see," she said.
"Today is such a special day.
I think my blue dress
will be just right."

After Lee had put on her dress,
she ran down the steps.
She thought her family
would be waiting for her.
Birthdays were always special in Lee's family.

Sure enough! They were at the table.
But they were not waiting for Lee.

They were laughing
and talking with each other.
They were eating, too.
They did not seem to know
when Lee came into the room.
They did not say a word
about her birthday.
They did not seem to remember.

This was such a special day.
And no one in Lee's family said
"Happy Birthday."

Lee thought about her birthday
as she walked to school.

"This is my very own birthday,"
she said. "And no one seems to care.
Today does not seem special to me.
No one has said a word about my birthday.
No one has made a birthday wish
for me. Not even Mom or Dad.
How could they forget?"

Lee was afraid she might cry.
But she didn't.

Lee tried to do her school work.
But all she could think about
was her birthday.

"Today does not seem like a birthday,"
she said to herself.
"There's nothing special about it.
No presents or wishes.
Not even a birthday cake!
Did Mom forget to make my cake?"

Each time Lee thought about Mom,
she was afraid she would cry.
But she didn't.

Mom always made a cake
for everyone's birthday.
Last year there had been six candles
on Lee's cake.
This year there should be seven.

Lee always made a secret wish
after she put out each candle.
Then she could open her presents.

Last year Mom had made the blue dress.
Lee had called it her birthday dress.

Each time Lee thought about her dress,
she was afraid she would cry.
She tried hard not to cry,
but this time she did.

Mother opened the door and asked,
"Why are you crying, dear?"

"Because it's my birthday,"
said Lee.
"And no one remembers.
A birthday without birthday wishes
does not seem very special."

"But today isn't your birthday,"
said her mother.
"Your birthday is tomorrow, dear."

"Tomorrow?" cried Lee.

Lee smiled a big smile.
Then she began to laugh.

"I'm glad," she said.
"I have been waiting all year
for my birthday.
I'm glad my birthday is not today.
I'm glad it's tomorrow."

A Birthday in Israel

This birthday child lives in Israel.

Her friends have come

to a birthday party in her home.

You can tell who the birthday child is.

She has a special place to sit.

The children do not dress up
for the party.
They have come right from school.

Some of the children have presents
for the birthday child.
But the presents will not be opened
until everyone goes home.

The children have fun at the party.
They sing songs and they play games
until it is time to eat.
But there is one thing
the children do not have.
They do not have a birthday cake.

A Birthday in Mexico

This birthday child lives in Mexico.
His family and friends have come to his birthday party.
They are all dressed up in their party clothes.

The party starts as soon as the people come.
It goes on all day.

The people bring presents
for the birthday child.
He will open these presents at the party.

The birthday child has a cake with candles.
He will put out these candles
after he has made three secret wishes.
Everyone will eat some of the cake.
Then they will start to sing songs
and play games.

Everyone will have fun at the party—
the birthday child,
his family,
and his friends.

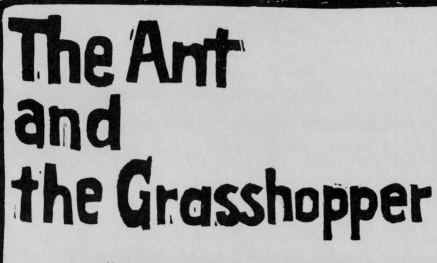

The Ant and the Grasshopper

All summer long a grasshopper played in the garden. He had fun hopping around and singing his song.

All summer long an ant worked in the garden. She did not have time to play. She had to look for food.

One day the grasshopper
saw the ant working.
He hopped over to talk with her.

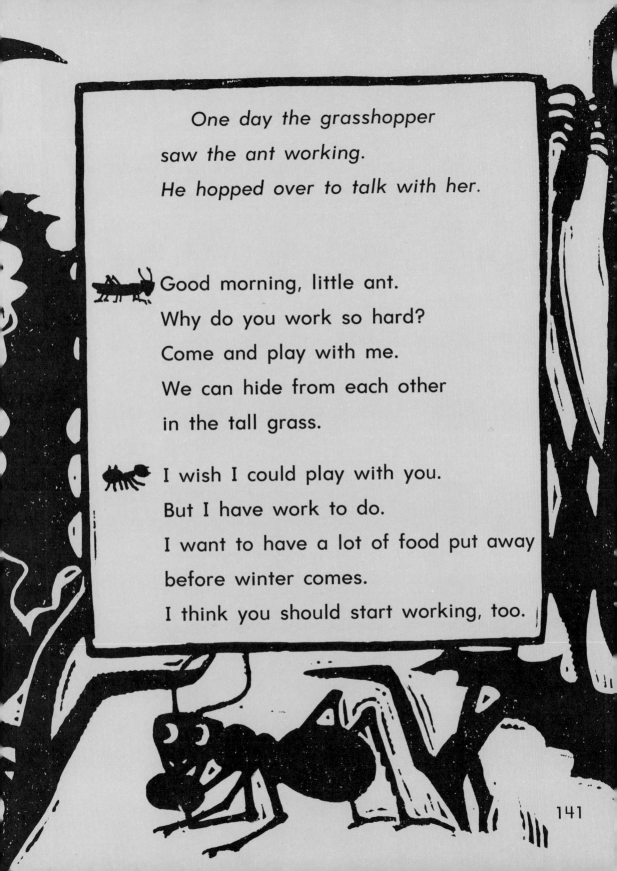 Good morning, little ant.
Why do you work so hard?
Come and play with me.
We can hide from each other
in the tall grass.

I wish I could play with you.
But I have work to do.
I want to have a lot of food put away
before winter comes.
I think you should start working, too.

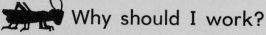 Why should I work?

Winter is a long way off.

There's lots of time to look for food.

Anyway I want to play in the grass.

Winter will bring ice and snow.

Then you will learn

that food is hard to find.

You had better start now, my friend.

Carry some food home today.

The grasshopper hopped away.

He did not carry any food with him.

He did not even look for food.

Soon winter came with its ice
and snow. The wind was cold.
Snow fell on the garden.
It fell on the grass and the trees.
It fell on the ant's house, too.

I had better stay inside today.
My house is warm.
And I have enough to eat.
I'm glad I don't have to carry food
in all this snow.

The snow was cold.
It fell on the grasshopper.
He wanted to get warm.
So he went to the ant's house.

 Please let me in.
There is nothing but ice and snow
out here. I am so cold.
And I have nothing to eat.
Let me have some food.
I will pay you back next summer.
Help me! Please help me!

 Why should I help you?
You did not work all summer.
And I did.
I told you that winter would come.
But you would not listen.

Oh, please help me.

Let me come in to get warm.

Let me have some food,

and I will sing for you.

We can play and have fun.

Both of us.

Listen to me, my friend.

Both of us like to eat,

so we must work.

You had better put some food away

in the summer time.

Then you will have something to eat

when the snow comes.

The ant went inside
her warm house and shut the door.
The grasshopper was left outside
in the wind and snow and ice.

Oh, me! Oh, my!
What shall I do?
I can't hop around on the ice.
I can't get warm in the snow.
I don't see any food in the garden.
Oh, what shall I do?

146

The grasshopper gave
one last look at the ant's house.
Then he hopped away.

Oh, me! Oh, my!
What shall I do?

What do you think the grasshopper
will do?

ANTS

Some ants live in the ground.
Some ants live in trees.
Some ants live under rocks.

Some ants live in tall buildings.
No one knows how they get so high
off the ground. But they do.

148

Some ants are big.

Some ants are not so big.

And some ants are very tiny.

But big or little,
all ants are alike
in some ways.

All ants have one head,
three pairs of legs,
and one pair of feelers.

Where are an ant's feelers?

Ants live together. But they are not alike
in the things they do. Some ants work.
Other ants do not work.

Some worker ants take care of the home.
Some worker ants leave home to get food.

Ants use their feelers
as they go about their work.
They use their feelers when they need help.

Sometimes a worker ant finds food
that is too big to carry home.
She may hit the other ants
with her feelers.
This lets the other ants know
that she needs help.

Soon many ants come running.
They work together to carry the food home.

GRASSHOPPERS

There are many kinds of grasshoppers.
Most of them live near the ground
where they find plants to eat.

One kind of grasshopper lives in trees.
It is called a katydid.
At night, a katydid sings a song
that seems to say . . .
      Katy did.
        She didn't.
          She did.

Grasshoppers have three pairs of legs.
They use all their legs when they walk.
They use their front legs
to hold food when they eat.
They use their back legs when they jump.
Their front legs are not as long
as their back legs.

Grasshoppers are very good jumpers.
They can jump a long way.

Did you ever hold a grasshopper
in your hand? It is hard to do.
A grasshopper will jump out
of your hand before you know it.

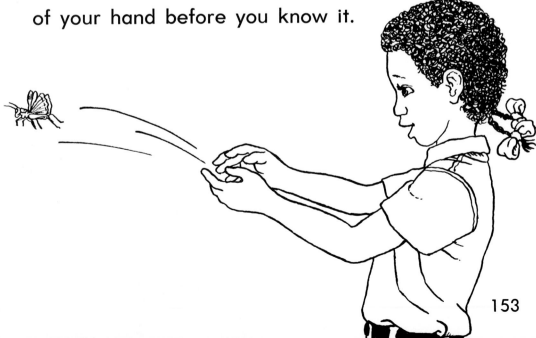

All grasshoppers are not alike,
but most of them have wings.
They use their wings when they fly.
Grasshoppers can fly fast,
but most of them don't fly very far.

Most grasshoppers sing a kind of song.
Some of them use their wings to do this.
Others use both feet and wings.

If you listen, you may hear
a grasshopper's song some summer day.
But try to listen late in the day.

Some grasshoppers lay eggs
in the late summer.
They lay the eggs in the ground
where they will stay all winter.

When winter is over,
the grasshoppers will sing again.
Listen, and you may hear their song . . .
Katy did.
She didn't.
She did.

Do You Remember?

Did you ever hear the song
a grasshopper sings?
Does he do it with his legs
or do it with his wings?

Did you ever see a little ant
walk in the door?
Does he walk on eight legs,
on six, or on four?

Ants Live Here

Ants live here
by the curb stone,
      see?
They worry a lot
about giants like
      me.

Lilian Moore

Little Ben

One morning Little Ben Beaver
left home all by himself.
He went across the pond
as fast as he could swim.
He wanted to pick something
for his mother.
He wanted to pick something
that would please her.

Little Ben found what he wanted.
It was pretty, so he picked it.
Then he started back across the pond.
He held the present in his mouth.

Little Ben was sure the present
would please his mother. It was pretty.
It would make up for his small tail.

Little Ben knew that his tail
was smaller than most beaver tails.
He knew it was smaller than the tails
his brothers and sisters had.

Little Ben's brothers and sisters
had fine big tails.
Their tails helped them to move fast
through the water.
They made fun of Little Ben
because he had such a little tail.

Sometimes Little Ben liked
to swim off by himself.
He could move through the water
as slow as he pleased.
But today he was in a hurry.
He had the present in his mouth
and he wanted to get it home.

While Little Ben was swimming,
his father was working across the pond.
His brothers and sisters
were playing near by.
They were swimming round and round.
Little Ben did not stop.
He was in a hurry.

Little Ben was swimming along
when he saw some children in a boat.
They were too close to his home!
What would they do to it?

"There's a beaver," called the boy.
"Let's see how close we can get to him."

"All right," said the girl.
"But don't hurt him."

The boat came close to Little Ben.
He began to move round and round.
This time he was not slow.

All at once Little Ben made a fast turn.
Then he went way down into the water.
Up he came on the other side of the boat.
And he still had his mother's present
in his mouth! It was not hurt at all.

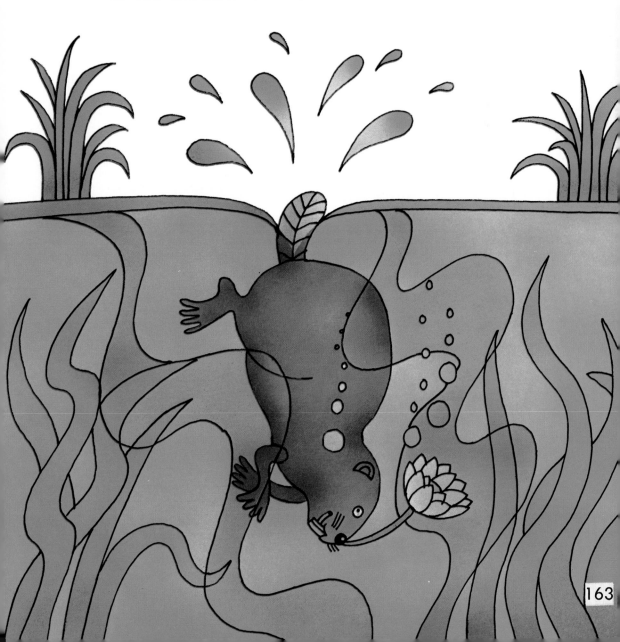

"There he is," called the girl.
"What does he have in his mouth?
Turn the boat around, so we can see."

But Little Ben went down
into the water again.
This time he came up
in another place.

He began to swim away
from his home in the pond.
The boat was not far
behind him.

164

Little Ben made many turns
as he led the children away
from the beaver home.
He went this way and that way
through the water.
He was always sure to keep
in front of the boat.
And the boat stayed close
behind him.

After a while
Little Ben stopped swimming.
He looked in front of him.
He looked behind him.
Then he saw what he had done.

He had led the way
to his brothers and sisters.
He had led the way
to his father, too.
They might get hurt!
What should he do?

Little Ben looked at his tail.
He thought about all the things
he could do with it.

"I use my tail when I hurry,"
he said to himself.
"I use my tail when I sit up tall.
I use it when I make a fast turn.
I have done all those things.
Now I must learn to make a big noise.
But I have such a little tail!"

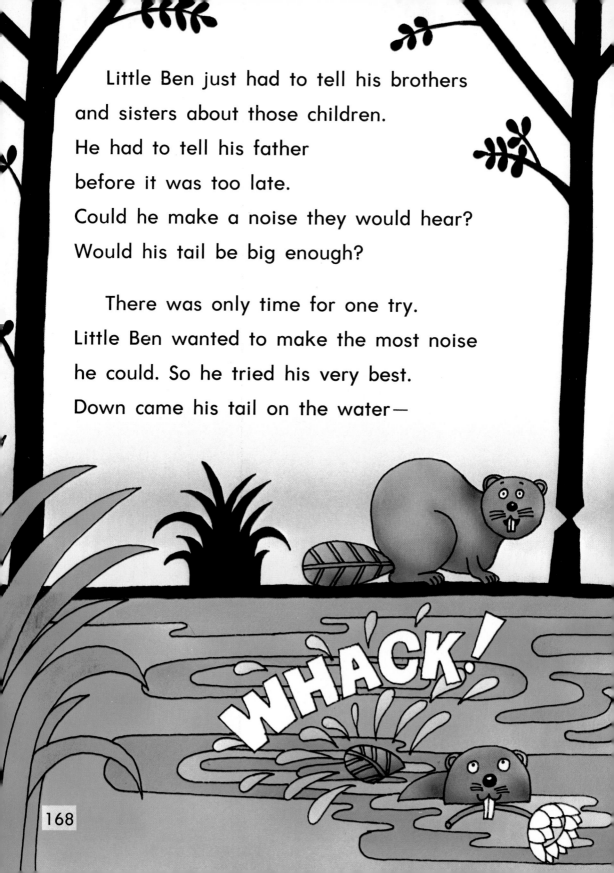

Little Ben just had to tell his brothers
and sisters about those children.
He had to tell his father
before it was too late.
Could he make a noise they would hear?
Would his tail be big enough?

There was only time for one try.
Little Ben wanted to make the most noise
he could. So he tried his very best.
Down came his tail on the water—

WHACK!

The noise was heard all over the pond.
It sent Little Ben's brothers and sisters
down into the water. It sent his father, too.

The children sat very still.
They had never heard such a noise.
They had never thought
beavers could move so fast.

Little Ben was surprised.
"That's the best noise I ever made,"
he said. "And I wasn't too late.
I sure made those beavers move."

Before long Little Ben was home again.

He was happy to be with his family.

He had the present in his mouth.

It was still pretty.

Father Beaver thought

Little Ben was very brave.

His brothers and sisters thought

he was brave, too.

They never made fun of his tail again.

Mother Beaver was glad that everyone
in her family was all right.
She knew that Little Ben was brave.
After all he was her own little beaver.
She thought he was the best little beaver
in the pond.

She was pleased with the present, too.
It was pretty, and Little Ben
had picked it just for her.

Little Ben sat back and smiled.

He knew that he was brave.

He knew that his present was pretty.

But better still,

he knew he could use his tail

to do most everything.

No one would ever

make fun of it again.

A Word Game

Read the words
in the first box.
Close your eyes
and try to remember them.
Then close your book
and get set to play
a word game.

First Box

alike	eggs
between	front
together	lot

The first player will say,
"One for the money.
Two for the show.
Three to get set.
And four to go,   ."

Second Box

pair	asleep
sent	lay
those	done

When your name is called,
say the words you remember.
Then call on another child.
Play the game again
with the words
in the second box
and the third box.

Third Box

eggs	pay
building	thank
lot	sent

Porcupines

Did you ever make porcupines?

Let's make some and find out why they are called porcupines.

Mix together in a bowl:
1 cup peanut butter
$\frac{1}{2}$ cup condensed milk
$\frac{1}{4}$ cup powdered sugar

Take part of the mix and roll it into a ball. Roll the ball in peanuts.

M-m-m-m! Now comes the best part!

Long Ago and Far Away

The Moon Child

Long ago in a far-away country,
there lived an old man and his wife.
The man was called Old Bamboo Cutter.
Each morning he would go out
and cut down bamboo plants.
He would make many things
out of these plants.

One day Old Bamboo Cutter
went out to cut plants.
Just as he always did.
Much to his surprise
he found one plant
that was not like
the other plants.
It was a shining bamboo plant.

"How beautiful!" he thought.
"I must cut this plant
with care."

Inside the shining bamboo plant
was a dear little girl.
She was not even as big as a bluebird.

Old Bamboo Cutter was pleased.

"This beautiful child must be a present
from the moon," he said.
"My dear wife will be happy,
for we have no children of our own.
I must hurry home and show her."

The man's good wife was pleased
to see the tiny child.

"Let us call her Shining Beauty,"
she said.
"She is more beautiful
than any other child.
We will love her
as if she were
our very own."

From that day on,
Old Bamboo Cutter found gold
in every bamboo plant he cut.
Before long he and his wife
had more gold than they could use.

Shining Beauty began to grow tall,
just as a bamboo plant does.
In a very little while
she was not tiny at all.

She loved Old Bamboo Cutter
and his wife.
And they loved her.

Three Wishes

Shining Beauty seemed to grow
more beautiful every day.
People came from far and near to see her.

There were three princes who came.
Each of them wanted the beautiful girl
for his wife. But Old Bamboo Cutter said No.
Until one day!
Then he said, "I will give Shining Beauty
to the prince who brings what she wishes
to see."

181

These are the things
Shining Beauty wished to see . . .

A gold ball from the home
of the dragon.

A blue feather from the tail
of the sky bird.

Something gold from a tree
in the Land of Never Grow Old.

The first prince
told Shining Beauty
that he would bring her
the gold ball.
So he got into a boat
and started across the water.

Soon he was close to the other side.
Then his boat hit a rock.
Down he went into the black water.

So the first prince did not even get
near the dragon's home.

The second prince told Shining Beauty
that he would bring her the blue feather.
Now this would be hard to do.
He had never been
to the top of the hill
where the sky bird lives.

The second prince
started up the hill.
Soon he was close
to the top.
Then he looked back.
Down he fell!

So the second prince
did not even get near
the sky bird.

The third prince said
he would bring something
from the tree of gold.
So off he started
for the Land of Never Grow Old.

The third prince had not gone far
when he came to the big green woods.
He had never walked
through these woods.
But he went right in.
Before long he was lost!

So the third prince
did not even get near
the tree of gold.

Now the king heard the story
about the lost princes.
He also heard the story
about Shining Beauty.

"I want to see her," he said to himself.
So off he went through the country.
He did not stop until he came
to the home of Old Bamboo Cutter.

The king asked Shining Beauty
to come with him. But her answer was No.
Not even the king
could have Shining Beauty
for his wife.

The Festival of the Full Moon

Night after night Shining Beauty
would stand on the hill looking at the moon.

"Why do you stand and look at the moon?"
asked Old Bamboo Cutter.

"I must go there soon," she answered.
"Tomorrow night is the festival of the full moon.
It is also the night when the moon people
are coming for me."

The moon was bright and full
on the night of the festival.
Men and women came
to stand on the hill.

All at once the little moon people
came down from the sky.

"Come with us, dear child,"
they said.

The moon people seemed to pull
Shining Beauty with their bright light.
Slowly, ever so slowly,
they took her up to the moon.

Old Bamboo Cutter made a fire
on top of the hill.

"Go find Shining Beauty," he said.
"Tell her that we will always love her."

The men and women saw the fire
go high into the sky.
They knew it would find Shining Beauty.
They would never forget her.

Why did the moon people come
for Shining Beauty?

Miguel

A long time ago
in a far-away country,
there lived a boy
named Miguel.

Miguel was always happy,
but he would never do
any work.

At last the day came
when his father said,
"Now you are big and strong.
You are no longer a child.
It is time for you to go out
and make your own way."

So Miguel took his cap
and started off.
He had not gone far
when he heard his mother calling.

191

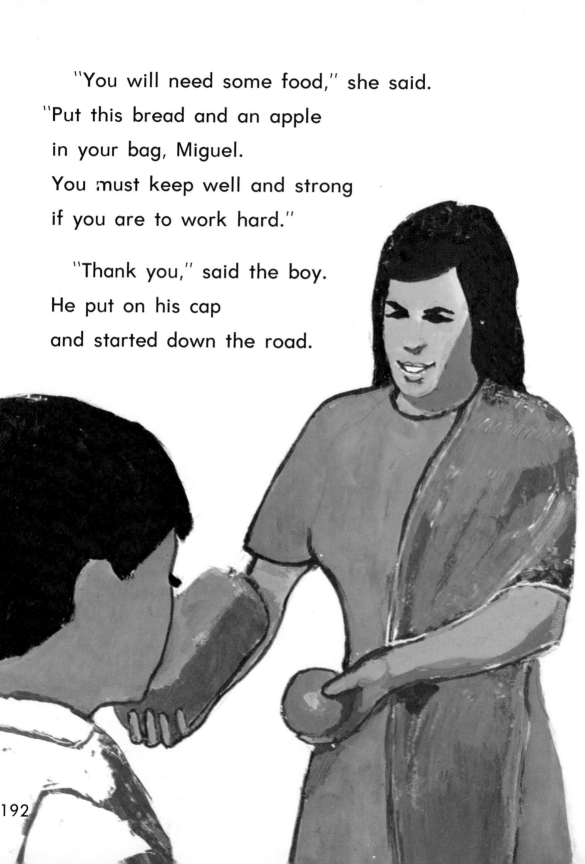

"You will need some food," she said.
"Put this bread and an apple
in your bag, Miguel.
You must keep well and strong
if you are to work hard."

"Thank you," said the boy.
He put on his cap
and started down the road.

Miguel walked along until he came
to a turn in the road.

"Which way shall I go?" he said.
"My feet can't go both ways.
I'll see which way they want to go.
I'll go where they take me."

So on he went . . .
walking,
walking,
walking.
Up one hill
and down another.

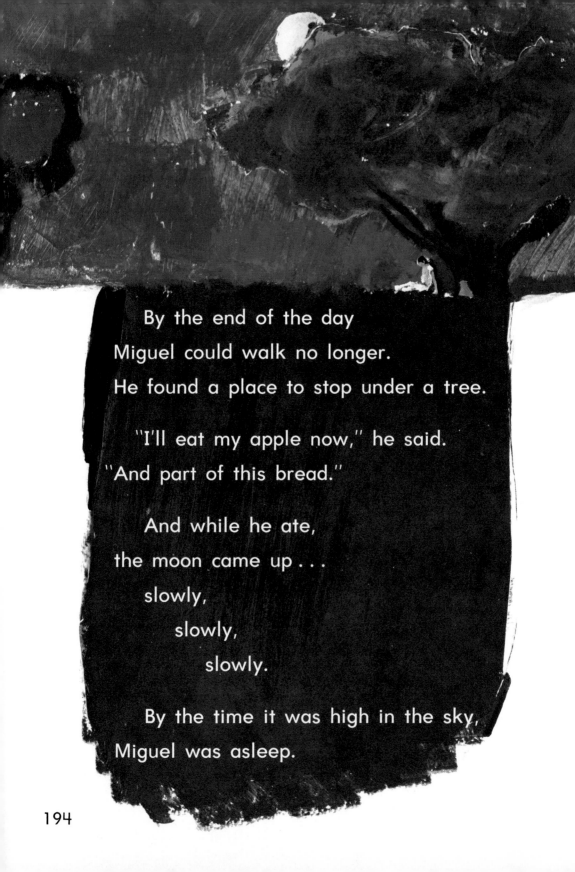

By the end of the day
Miguel could walk no longer.
He found a place to stop under a tree.

"I'll eat my apple now," he said.
"And part of this bread."

And while he ate,
the moon came up . . .
slowly,
     slowly,
          slowly.

By the time it was high in the sky,
Miguel was asleep.

Miguel and the Dragon

The next morning Miguel was up
with the sun.
He opened his bag to see
what he could find to eat.

The apple was gone,
and part of the bread.

"I'll eat the bread," he said.
"Then I must be on my way."

So that was the end
of his food.

Once more Miguel started off
with the cap on his head
and the bag in his hand.

The sun was hot,
so he left the road
and went into the woods.

And there . . .
he came face to face
with a dragon!

Miguel was scared.
He started to run away
when he saw a big stick.

He picked up the stick.
Then he heard a soft voice say,
"Oh, please don't hit me.
I'm not a bad dragon.
I won't hurt you.
I have never hurt anyone."

197

Miguel put his arm down,
and the stick fell to the ground.
"I thought you wanted to fight," he said.

"Well, I don't," said the dragon
in the same soft voice.
"I don't like to fight like most animals do.
I'm not brave enough."

"It's too hot to fight," said Miguel.

The dragon went over to the river
to get a drink of water.
Miguel walked close behind him.

"I thought all dragons were bad,"
said Miguel. "I was afraid of you."

"Don't be afraid," said the dragon.
"I'm not bad and I'm not brave.
I'm just timid."

"Why do you say that?" asked Miguel.

"Sit down and I'll tell you,"
answered the dragon.

The Timid Dragon

"Once I was brave," said the dragon.
"I thought I could do most anything.
But one day I met a lion
not far from this river.
The lion had something in its mouth.
I was sure it was another animal.
I wanted to catch an animal, too."

"Did you?" asked Miguel.

"Well, I tried to," answered the dragon.
"I jumped with all my might.
But the animal turned out to be a rock.

And seven
of my teeth
fell out!"

"Did your teeth hurt?" asked Miguel.

"No, but my mouth did," said the dragon.

He went to get another drink.
Then he said, "I always wanted to jump
from tree to tree.
Just like a monkey does.
So one day I was all set to jump."

"Could you do it?" asked Miguel.

"Well I tried," said the dragon.
But I fell to the ground with a thud.

And I lost
some more
of my teeth!"

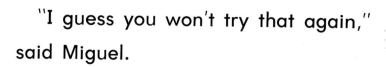

"I guess you won't try that again,"
said Miguel.

"No, I won't," said the dragon.
"And I won't try to fly like a bird.
One day I was all set to do it.
I took off from the top
of that high rock.
Then I began to fall . . .

fast!

I landed on the ground
with a thud.

And that was
the end
of my teeth!"

"What a long way to fall!"
said Miguel.

"Yes, it was," said the dragon
in his soft dragon voice.
"I won't ever try to fly again.
Or to catch another animal.
Or to jump from tree to tree.
I'm just too timid."

"I thought you wanted
to fight," said Miguel.
"I thought you were mean."

"I'm not mean," said the dragon.
"And I'm too timid to fight."

By now he and Miguel
were standing face to face.

Miguel said, "I am looking
for a new place to live.
Come along and help me look.
What do you say, Friend?"

"I'll come," answered the dragon.
"I'll even let you ride on my back."

"That will be fine," said Miguel.
"I'll be glad to ride!"

So off they went through the woods . . .
the dragon walking,
and Miguel riding.

For all we know,
they are still looking
for a new place
where Miguel can make
his own way.

Bobo

Once upon a time
there was a boy named Bobo.
He lived with his mother
on a small farm.

Bobo always tried to do
as he was told.
Sometimes this was hard,
but Bobo did his best.

One day Bobo's mother had to drive
into the city.

"Find a hen and dress it for our dinner,"
she called. "Make sure it is big and fat.
Hurry now! I won't be gone long."

Bobo saw her drive away from the farm.
Then he ran into the yard to catch a fat hen.

At five o'clock
his mother came home
from the city.

"Did you dress the hen?"
she asked.

"Yes, I did," answered Bobo.
"A big fat one.
It was hard to do,
but I did my best."

And there
upon the table
sat a fat hen!

Bobo and the Light

One night Bobo was playing
with the dog. "Roll over," he said.
But the dog would not roll over.
It ran across the floor after a ball.
Then round and round it went with the ball
in its mouth. Bobo was not far behind.

"It's ten o'clock," called his mother.
"Get up from the floor and put out the light.
You should have been in bed
long ago."

Now Bobo always tried to do as he was told.
So he picked up the light and put it outside.

The next morning his mother asked,
"Where is the light? I can't find it."

"You told me to put it out," answered Bobo.
"So I did."

Bobo and the Gray Cap

Another time Bobo's mother called him in from the yard.

"Take this wash to Mrs. Hopnot," she said. "She lives in the city on Groan Street."

Bobo liked to drive to the city. So he was glad to take the wash. He put on his fine new cap and started down the road.

Bobo had not gone far
when he heard his mother call.

"I think it's going to rain," she said.
"Don't let any rain get
on your new gray cap."

"I won't," said the boy.

It did not take long for Bobo
to drive to the city.
He found the house on Groan Street
and gave the wash to Mrs. Hopnot.
Then he started the ride
back to the farm.

Just as he got to the top of a hill,
the rain began to fall.
He pulled the gray cap down
to keep his ears dry.
Then he remembered
what his mother had told him.

"My cap!" said Bobo
to himself.
"I can't let the rain fall
on my new gray cap!"

He took it off and held his hands
over his ears to keep them dry.
Then he ran to the river.
Before you could say one word,
Bobo was in the water.

"I'll hold my cap in the river," he said.
"To keep the rain off." And he did.

Bobo and the Door

The next day Bobo's mother said,
"I must drive to the city again.
Take care of the door while I am gone."

Bobo waited all day for his mother
to come home. It began to get late.
By ten o'clock he thought
he had better look for her.

He pulled his gray cap over his ears
and started down the road.
Then he remembered
about the door.

"I must take care of the door,"
said Bobo. "I'll not leave it here."

So he started off again,
with the door upon his back.

After a time he saw some men
going into the woods.
They were carrying a bag
between them.

"Robbers!" said Bobo.
"They look mean."
He was scared.

It didn't take long
for Bobo to get into a tree.
This was hard to do
with the door upon his back.
But Bobo was a strong boy.

Down on the ground,
the robbers opened the bag.
It was full of gold!
Bright yellow gold!

Bobo listened as the men
began to count the gold.

"One for me and one for you,"
counted the first robber.

"And one for me!" cried Bobo.

"Who said that?" asked the second robber.

The men listened, but heard nothing.

The first robber began to count again.
"This one for me," he said.
"This one for you."

"And one for me!" cried Bobo.

"Who said that?" called a robber
in his big strong voice.
"I'll snip off his ears if I catch him."

"That robber is mean," thought Bobo.

He began to shake so hard,

the door fell from his back.

Right on top of the robbers.

"A ghost!" they cried.

The robbers ran to the river
and jumped in.
They have never been
in that part of the woods again.

Bobo ran back to the farm
as fast as his legs would take him.

His mother smiled when she saw
the bag full of gold.
"You are a good boy," she said.
"But what about the door?"

"It helped me take care
of some mean robbers," said Bobo.
"Tomorrow I'll take care
of the door."

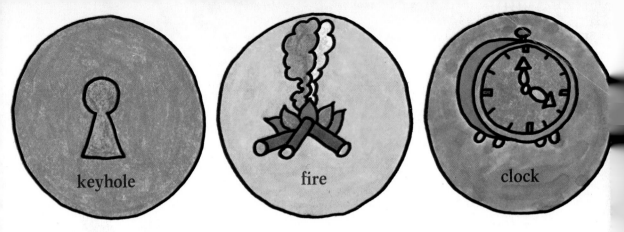

keyhole fire clock

Do You Know?

1. What has no arms, no legs, no feet,
   and goes higher than a building?

2. What goes through a door
   but never goes in and never comes out?

3. What has ears but cannot hear?

4. What was made years ago
   and can also be made today?

5. What falls in winter but never gets hurt?

6. What has a pair of hands
   but can't hold anything?

snow

ear of corn

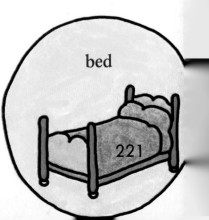

bed

221

What Am I?

1. What has an arm
   but can't pick it up?

2. What can grow head down
   and feet up?

3. What has a face
   but can't see?

4. What can a girl hold
   but not in her hands?

5. What is taller when it sits
   than when it stands?

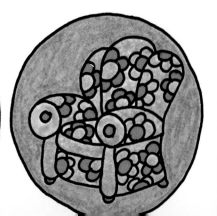

A Word Game

"Ride away, Timid Dragon!"
called Miguel.
"Which way shall we go?"

also   apple   bad   fire   hot

also   arm   bright

apple   bad   o'clock

wash   ears   soft

fat   fire   stand

love   floor   hot   roll   set   sun   street

done   wash strong

sun   street sun

upon   story

soft   together

story

street bread   which

223

(Acknowledgments continued from page 2.)

Grosset & Dunlap, Inc., for "Robber in the Woods." Adapted from ROBBER RACCOON. Story by Thomas Lawrence. Pictures by Richard Cuffari. Copyright © 1971 by Grosset & Dunlap, Inc. Published by Grosset & Dunlap, Inc.

The Society of Authors for permission to use the poem "Some One," by Walter de la Mare. Reprinted by permission of The Literary Trustees of Walter de la Mare, and The Society of Authors as their representative.

Steck-Vaughn Company for an adaptation of "Just for Manuel." From *Just for Manuel* by Doris Hampton. Copyright © 1971 by Steck-Vaughn Company.

United States Committee for UNICEF for "Moon Child." Adapted from "Kaguya-Hime (The Story of Shining Beauty)." From *Hi Neighbor*, Book II.

Henry Z. Walck, Inc., for "Little Ben." Based on the story LITTLE BEN © copyright Catherine Barr 1960. Used by permission of Henry Z. Walck, Inc.

The World Publishing Company for the adaptation "Little Hippo." Reprinted by permission of The World Publishing Company from THE SECRET HIDING PLACE by Rainey Bennett. Copyright © 1960 by Rainey Bennett.

224